"One wheel," said Chip.

"Look," said Chip.

"One wheel."

"Look," said Mum.

"I am on two wheels."

"Look at me," said Kipper.

"I am on three wheels."

"Look at me," said Biff.

"I am on four wheels."

"Look at Dad," said Mum.

"He is on one wheel."

"Oh no," said Dad.
"No wheels."